The Dinosaur

Edited by Gillian Doherty
With thanks to Darren Naish for information about dinosaurs

The Dinosaur

Anna Milbourne

Illustrated by Mandy Field

Designed by Laura Fearn and Laura Parker

Nobody has ever seen a real live dinosaur.

But long, long ago, before the
world had cars or roads...

before there were
houses or cities...

and even before the very
first people were born...

a big, brown dinosaur egg
lay at the edge of a huge forest.

From inside the egg came a tap, tap, tap.
Then there was a
CRACK!

And out climbed a baby stegosaurus.

One by one, more eggs broke open.

His brothers and sisters
were hatching out too.

The baby stegosaurus
was very, **very** hungry.

He ate whatever
he could find.

He ate crunchy cones and ferny leaves,
and chewy fruit from spiky plants.

Each day he grew **bigger** and **bigger**...

until he was almost as big as an elephant.

Soon, the stegosaurus was so big,
he had trouble fitting through the trees.

So he poked his head out of the forest, to see what the world was like outside.

It seemed safe enough.

It was an **enormous** allosaurus
with **enormous** allosaurus teeth...

and it wanted to eat him up!

Quickly, the stegosaurus
swung his spiky tail...

Thump!

It hit the allosaurus
right on the nose.

The allosaurus growled
and left him alone.

The stegosaurus felt big and strong.
Now he could take care of himself.

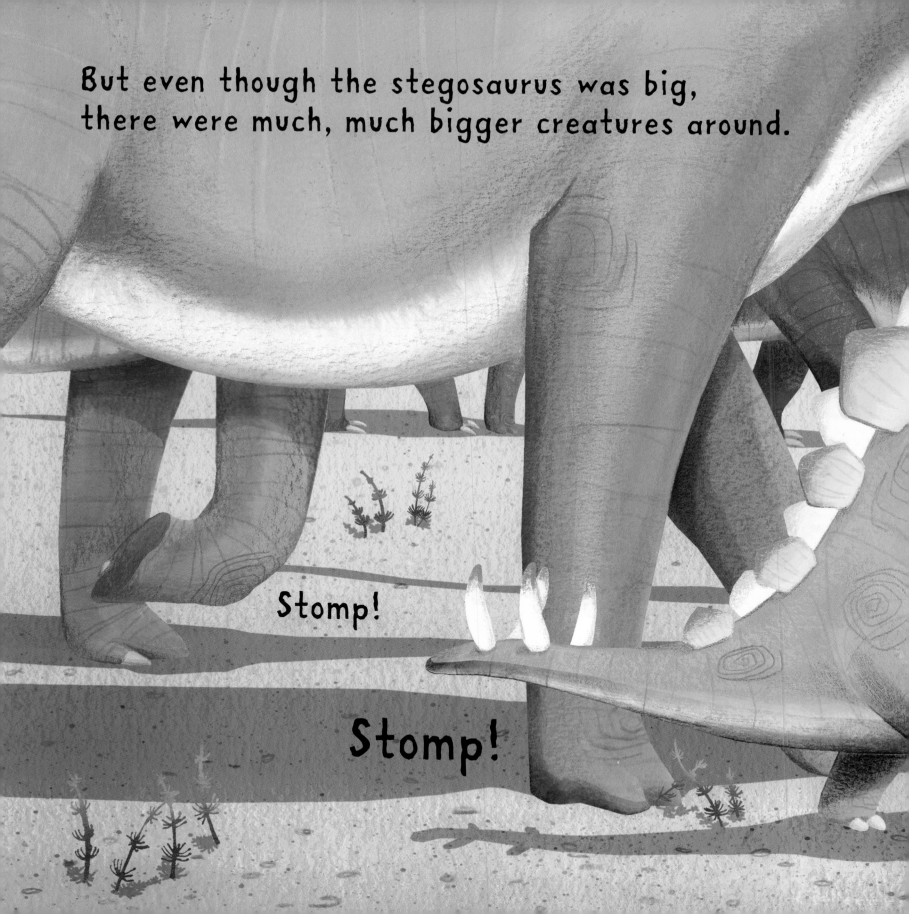

But even though the stegosaurus was big,
there were much, much bigger creatures around.

Stomp!

Stomp!

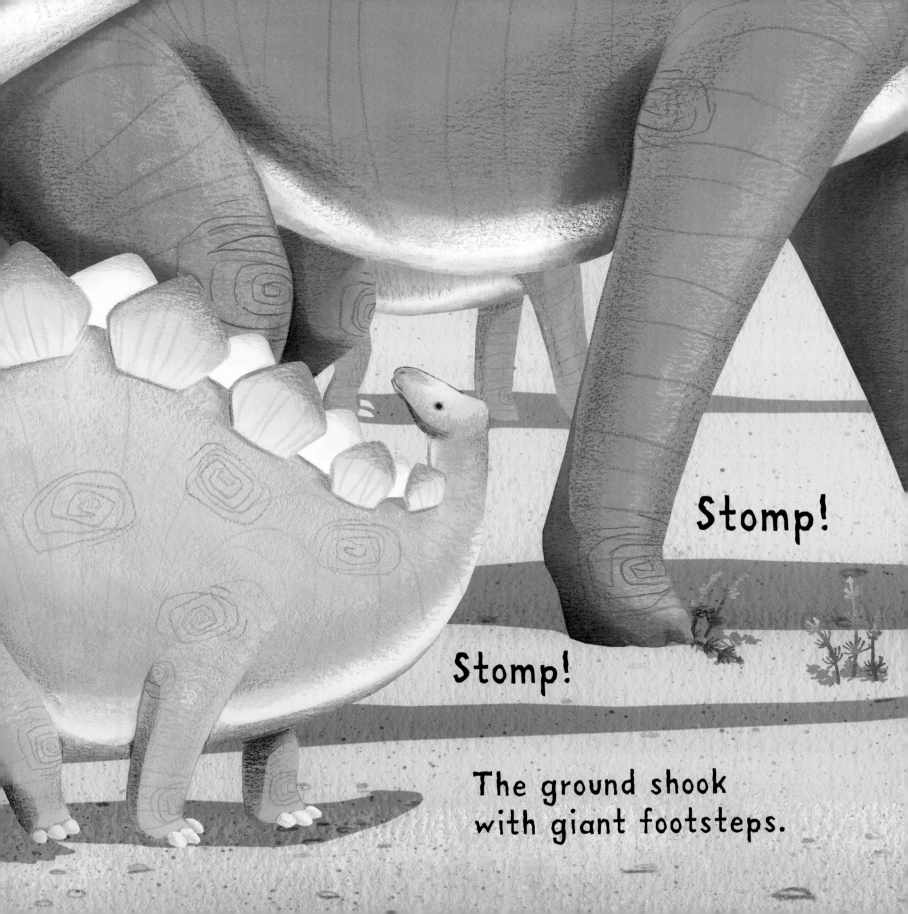

Stomp!

Stomp!

The ground shook
with giant footsteps.

A whole herd of diplodocuses
was marching across the plains.

Luckily, they only ate leaves...

NOT stegosauruses.

The world was different
when dinosaurs lived.

What would it be like
if they were still alive?

They would
block up roads...

Maybe it's just as well
that only their dusty
old bones are left.

This book belongs to:

....

....

Quarto is the authority on a wide range of topics.

Quarto educates, entertains and enriches the lives of our readers—enthusiasts and lovers of hands-on living.

www.quartoknows.com

Author: Amanda Askew
Illustrator: Ayesha L. Rubio
Designer: Victoria Kimonidou
Editor: Ellie Brough

© 2018 Quarto Publishing plc

This paperback edition first published in 2019 by QED Publishing,
an imprint of The Quarto Group.
The Old Brewery, 6 Blundell Street,
London N7 9BH, United Kingdom.
T (0)20 7700 6700 F (0)20 7700 8066
www.QuartoKnows.com

A catalogue record for this book is available from
the British Library.

ISBN 978 1 78603 936 1

Manufactured in Shenzhen, China PP022019

9 8 7 6 5 4 3 2 1